Linda Cummings

animate

PRACTICES

ILLUSTRATED BY
PAUL SOUPISET
& CHRIS TAYLOR

WRITTEN BY
CARLA BARNHILL
& TONY JONES

SPARK
HOUSE
wearesparkhouse.org | MINNEAPOLIS, MN

CONTRIBUTORS
BRIAN MCLAREN, SARA MILES,
MIKE SLAUGHTER, PHYLLIS TICKLE,
SHANE CLAIBORNE, ENUMA OKORO,
DOUG PAGITT

JOURNAL ILLUSTRATION
BY PAUL SOUPISET, WITH ADDITIONAL
ILLUSTRATION BY CHRIS TAYLOR,
FOR TOOLBOX STUDIOS, INC.

JOURNAL WRITERS
CARLA BARNHILL, TONY JONES

SPARKHOUSE TEAM
ANDREW DEYOUNG, HEIDI HOGG, TONY JONES,
TIMOTHY PAULSON, KRISTOFER SKRADE

TOOLBOX STUDIOS TEAM
PAUL SOUPISET, CHRIS TAYLOR,
STACY THOMAS

VIDEO TEAM
KYLE ISENHOWER OF ISENHOWER
PRODUCTIONS, SHANE NELSON OF
OMNI-FUSION MEDIA PRODUCTION

SPECIAL THANKS TO PHOTOGRAPHER
COURTNEY PERRY

THE PAPER USED IN THIS PUBLICATION
MEETS THE MINIMUM REQUIREMENTS
OF AMERICAN NATIONAL STANDARD FOR
INFORMATION SCIENCES — PERMANENCE OF
PAPER FOR PRINTED LIBRARY MATERIALS,
ANSI Z329 . 48 -1984

MANUFACTURED IN THE U.S.A.

16 15 14 1 2 3 4 5 6 7 8 9 10

ISBN 978-1-4514-9006-0

animate
PRACTICES

This journal is pretty amazing to look at. It's got gorgeous illustrations created by phenomenally talented artists and thought-provoking words from some of the most innovative Christian thinkers and practitioners in the country.

But it's not done, not by a long shot.

The pages of this journal aren't meant to sit there and look pretty. They are intended to be a starting point for your images, your words, your phenomenal creations and though-provoking ideas. So scribble on the pages, write down your thoughts, color outside of the lines—seriously. Make this thing your own. No one is going to look over your shoulder to check your work. No one is handing out gold stars to the student who gets the right answers. Really, no one is convinced there are right answers.

So instead of focusing on answers, *Animate:Practices* is starting a conversation. These sessions explore the role seven spiritual practices—prayer, community, service, money, the sacraments, worship, and food—have played in the history of our faith and how they might enrich our lives today. You're going to be asked to try some things you've maybe never tried before, like confessing your sin to a friend and sharing your money with a stranger and having a meal with someone you hardly know. It might be weird. It might be unsettling. It might push you out of your routines.

||: engage→reflect :||

But don't worry. Your fellow travelers are people who've been walking this path for a while—people like Shane Claiborne and Sara Miles and Brian McLaren and Phyllis Tickle. You'll hear how they've worked through the challenges these practices present and get their thoughts on what even the most ancient practices might look like for us today.

As you work through each session, remember that you are encouraged to speak up when you think the trail is veering off. If something strikes you as worth talking about, talk about it. If something else feels uninspiring, go ahead and skip that part. This is your journey and you get to decide when to stop and linger and when to keep moving.

We hope you end each session with some ink on your fingers. The beautiful pages of this journal aren't meant to stay pristine. They are a springboard meant to plunge you into your own imagination. So doodle, write notes, add your thoughts and questions. Mess with the ideas and the images and see where the conversation takes you.

In the days between sessions, you'll be moving deeper into the practices discussed in the session. As you do, we invite you to join in the growing Animate community. We've put together a host of social media platforms you can use to share your experiences, connect with the creators of Animate:Practices, and hear from other churches and groups using this series around the country.

Connect with us on Facebook, Twitter, and Pinterest and tell us what you're thinking and how these practices are shaping you:

FACEBOOK.COM/ANIMATESERIES

TWITTER.COM/SHANIMATE

PINTEREST.COM/WEARESPARKHOUSE

We can't wait to find out where Animate takes you!

PRAYER | ORIENTED TOWARD GOD
BRIAN MCLAREN

BRIAN MCLAREN

BRIAN MCLAREN IS AN AUTHOR, SPEAKER, AND FLY FISHERMAN. HIS MOST RECENT BOOK IS *WE MAKE THE ROAD BY WALKING* (2014). HE CAN ALSO BE FOUND ON A GOOGLE EARTH IMAGE OF A SMALL LAKE NEAR HIS HOME IN FLORIDA.

BRIAN TALKS ABOUT HOW HE FOUND COMFORT IN PRAYER WHEN HIS FROG WENT MISSING. WRITE A BIT ABOUT A TIME WHEN PRAYER WAS A COMFORT TO YOU.

HOME	EVENT	094	AWAY
O	HEAT	001	O
	POSITION	022	

Brian also talks about the voices that tell us how prayer "ought" to be—longer, more sincere, more theologically correct. Write about the ways those voices have affected your prayer life.

GO

WaKe UP.

TUNe UP.

"OUR FATHER IN
HEAVEN, HALLOWED
BE YOUR NAME."

"YOUR KINGDOM COME,
YOUR WILL BE DONE
ON EARTH AS IT IS
IN HEAVEN."

How might these prayer moves

ASK. RE-ENTER.

"FORGIVE US OUR SINS
as we FORGIVE THOSE
WHO SIN against US."

"LEAD US NOT INTO
TEMPTATION, BUT
DELIVER US FROM EVIL."

be life-giving for you?

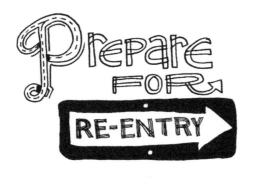

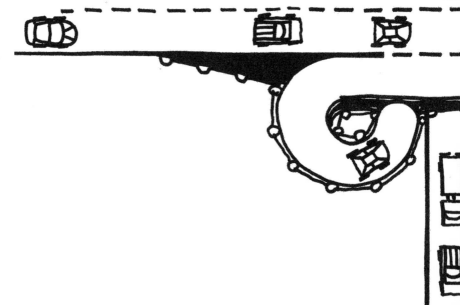

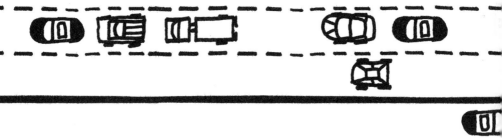

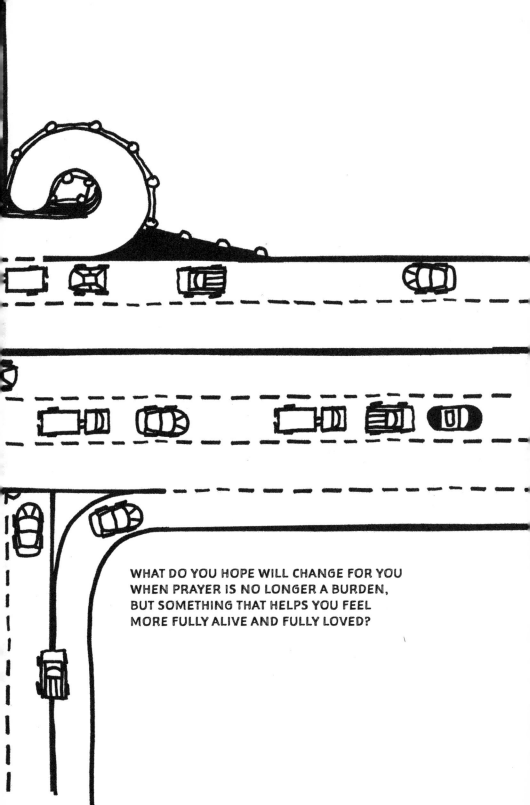

WHAT DO YOU HOPE WILL CHANGE FOR YOU
WHEN PRAYER IS NO LONGER A BURDEN,
BUT SOMETHING THAT HELPS YOU FEEL
MORE FULLY ALIVE AND FULLY LOVED?

DAY 1

This week, you'll be focusing on following Brian's four moves to help you develop a more meaningful prayer life. Before you start tomorrow, spend some time writing down your thoughts about prayer. What role does it play in your life? What role would you like it to play? What do you think prayer is for?

"THE PRAYER DOES NOT CHANGE GOD, BUT IT CHANGES THE ONE WHO OFFERS IT."
~ SØREN KIERKEGAARD

animate

The first move Brian suggests is to "wake up" to the mystery of God and the wonder of being part of God's family. Today, make an effort to see God's presence in the world around you. What did you notice that you haven't before? Where or how did you feel connected to God today?

" I CANNOT HELP THINKING THAT THE BEST WAY OF **KNOWING GOD** IS TO LOVE MANY THINGS. Love THIS PERSON, THIS FRIEND, THIS THING, WHATEVER YOU LIKE, AND YOU WILL BE ON THE RIGHT ROAD TO UNDERSTANDING HIM BETTER. "

— VINCENT VAN GOGH

DAY 3

Today, you'll focus on the "tune up" aspect of prayer. As you move through the day, consider how you can align your hopes, your desires, even your attitude with God's. How does this kind of realignment feel? What are some places or relationships in your life where it's a challenge to figure out how to be in tune with God?

"PRAYER IS PUTTING ONESELF IN THE HANDS OF GOD, AT HIS DISPOSITION, AND LISTENING TO HIS VOICE IN THE DEPTH OF OUR HEARTS."
— MOTHER TERESA

The "Ask" part of prayer is a tough one. It involves accepting God's grace and offering that grace to others. If you've been holding on to an old grudge, use this as an opportunity to let it go. If you're struggling with this, ask God to help you release the pain and the resentment that can build up in relationships so you can experience the healing that comes from offering forgiveness. Either way, write down the name of the person or the situation you need to forgive below.

"FORGIVENESS IS THE NAME OF LOVE PRACTICED AMONG PEOPLE WHO LOVE POORLY. the hard truth is that all people love poorly. WE NEED TO FORGIVE AND BE FORGIVEN EVERY DAY, EVERY HOUR, INCREASINGLY. THIS IS THE great WORK OF LOVE AMONG THE fellowship OF THE WEAK THAT IS THE HUMAN FAMILY."
—HENRI NOUWEN

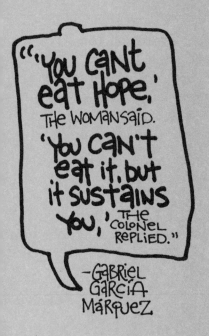

"'You can't eat Hope,' the woman said. 'You can't eat it, but it sustains you,' the colonel replied."

—Gabriel García Márquez

Today, you'll "prepare for re-entry." Come up with a short saying—a kind of mantra—and use it to pull you out of today's temptations to live in anger or fear or frustration. It could be as simple as "Lead me" or "Peace" or even "Breathe." Use that word or phrase when you feel stress or anxiety coming on as a reminder to tap into the peace and serenity God offers us. How did this word or phrase help you today?

DAY 6

Now that you've practiced all four moves individually, try using them together in a more intentional way. Find a time today to focus fully on the moves—Wake Up, Tune Up, Ask, and Prepare for Re-entry—in a way that flows for you. It could look like a silent prayer or meditation, talking out loud to God in your car, or just a subtle shift in perspective. Notice what changes in you as you incorporate these moves into your day. Write about some of those changes here.

"Likewise, THE SPIRIT HELPS US IN OUR WEAKNESS; FOR WE DO NOT KNOW HOW TO PRAY AS WE OUGHT, BUT THE VERY SPIRIT INTERCEDES WITH sighs TOO DEEP FOR WORDS."
— ROMANS 8:26

animate

FOOD | EATING, WITH JESUS
SARA MILES

SARA MILES IS A CHEF
TURNED JOURNALIST
TURNED CHURCH LEADER
TURNED AUTHOR. SHE HAS
WRITTEN ABOUT FOOD AND
COMMUNITY IN HER BOOKS
TAKE THIS BREAD, *JESUS
FREAK*, AND *CITY OF GOD*.
SHE LIVES AND WORKS IN
SAN FRANCISCO.

animate

CAN KALE SAVE?

Sara pushes at our ideas about the moral values we give to food. Have you ever found yourself judging other people based on what they eat?

WHETHER YOU HAVE TOO LITTLE OF IT OR TOO MUCH OF IT, IT'S TEMPTING TO IDOLIZE FOOD. TALK ABOUT WAYS YOU'VE FALLEN INTO THAT TEMPTATION.

FOR YOUR SOUL

THIS GRINDER MAY HAVE BEEN USED TO GRIND NON-ORGANIC BEANS

It might surprise you to hear Sara say that the abundance of good food can be as bad for your soul as the scarcity of food. What do you think she means?

THE OLD TESTAMENT IS FULL OF RULES AND RESTRICTIONS ABOUT WHAT TO EAT, HOW TO PREPARE IT, WHEN TO EAT IT, AND WHO TO EAT IT WITH. THESE DIETARY LAWS WERE, AND CONTINUE TO BE, CENTRAL TO MANY RELIGIONS. BUT LIKE ANY GOOD THING, THEY CAN ALSO BE MISUSED AND TURNED INTO WAYS TO DECIDE WHO IS IN AND WHO IS OUT.

When he ate with tax collectors and prostitutes, Jesus brought about the banquet feast that Isaiah spoke of. He made it clear that the kingdom feast is open to everyone.

are Thirsty, Drink

WHAT DIETARY RULES OR RESTRICTIONS DO YOU HAVE? HAVE THEY EVER GOTTEN IN THE WAY OF YOUR RELATIONSHIPS?

This week, you'll eat a meal with someone you don't normally eat with. The idea is to use food as a means toward building relationships and creating connections with people who aren't in your regular circle of friends and family. As you work through the steps each day, pay attention to how you're feeling about the prospect of sharing food with a relative stranger. Write down some initial thoughts about making this happen. Does it make you nervous? Excited? Something else?

"Welcome those who are weak in faith, but not for the purpose of quarreling over opinions. Some believe in eating anything, while the weak eat only vegetables. Those who eat must not despise those who abstain, & those who abstain must not pass judgment on those who eat; for God has welcomed them." ROMANS 14:1-3

Today, figure out who you'd like to invite to share a meal with you and what that meal might entail. Do you want to invite this person to your home? Include your family? Bring a meal to share at work? Once you know who you're inviting and what you're inviting them to, send an email, make a call, or stop by her office to make the offer. They might think it's weird. It is a little bit weird. But you can handle it. Write down your plans.

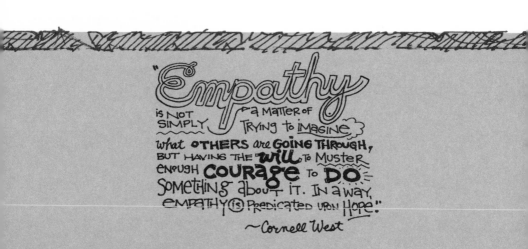

"Empathy is not simply a matter of trying to imagine what others are going through, but having the will to muster enough courage to do something about it. In a way, empathy is predicated upon Hope."

~Cornell West

LENTIL SOUP

- 6 cups vegetable broth
- 2 cups dry green lentils
- 2 cups diced canned tomatoes
- 1 cup finely chopped yellow onion
- 1/2 cup finely CHOPPED carrot
- 1/2 CUP FINELY Chopped CELERY
- 1/2 cup finely chopped zucchini
- 4 minced garlic cloves
- 1 tsp DRIED basil
- 1 tsp DRIED thyme
- 1/2 tsp ground coriander
- salt & freshly ground black pepper, to taste garnish with FRESH Herbs

Saute onions, carrots, celery, zucchini and garlic until onions are translucent. Add the lentils, tomatoes, broth & spices. STIR to combine.

Increase the HIGH heat and bring JUST to a boil. REDUCE the heat to LOW, cover with a lid and cook at a low simmer for an hour.

ADD more BROTH if stew becomes too thick.

~ from gluten-free-vegan girl.com

Use today to plan your menu. Keep the meal simple so you're not focused on the food but on the company.

·DAY 4·

Time for the details. Shop for groceries, clean up the house, prep for your guest. But most importantly, be sure to connect with this person again—say hello, drop a short email telling the person you're looking forward to your meal together. This is probably uncharted territory for both of you, so go ahead and acknowledge that out loud. So how are you feeling as the day grows closer?

"If you can't feed one hundred people, then feed just one." ~Mother Teresa

As you share your meal, don't be afraid to ask odd questions like, "What song always makes you want to sing along?" or "What was your favorite treat when you were a kid?" Remember that the goal here is to get to know the other person and let them get to know you. Sharing food has an interesting way of making that easier. After the meal, write out some thoughts on how it went and what you discovered about this person.

"Cooking is like LOVE. it should be entered into with ABANDON or not at all."

~ Harriet Van Horne

Send a thank-you note (a real note, not an email) to tell your dinner guest how much you enjoyed your time together. Take some time today to reflect on this experience. What did you discover about the ways food helps us connect with others? Would you do it again?

"eating WITH THE FULLEST PLEASURE — pleasure, THat is, that DOES NOT DEPEND ON IGNºRANCE — is perHaps THe profounDest enactment of our

CONNECTION

WitH THe WORLD. IN THis pleasure we experience & celebrate our DepenDence anD our gratituDe, For we are LiviNg From Mystery, From Creatures we DiD Not Make AND POWERS We CANNOT COMPreHenD." — WenDell Berry

animate

WORSHIP | SEEKING GOD'S PRESENCE
MIKE SLAUGHTER

HEALTHY...

COMMUNAL...

RESTORATIVE

WORTHY...

MiKe SLaUghTeR

MIKE SLAUGHTER IS THE PASTOR OF GINGHAMSBURG CHURCH NEAR DAYTON, OHIO. HE IS THE AUTHOR OF *HIJACKED: RESPONDING TO THE PARTISAN CHURCH DIVIDE* AND *CHANGE THE WORLD: RECOVERING THE MESSAGE AND MISSION OF JESUS.*

I SURVIVED, BUT NOTHING IN MY LIFE stayed the same.

Think about a dramatic life experience that's caused you to change course— a health scare, a family crisis, a surprising job offer. What had to change in your life as a result?

In the history of the faith, worship has looked like all kinds of things, from celebratory singing and dancing (Psalm 100:1–5), to small groups of people gathering to pray and eat together, to monastics centering their lives completely on God.
The Apostle Paul even talks about caring for our bodies as an act of worship (Romans 12:1–2).

AWE

WORS

HOLY

WHEN YOU HEAR THE WORD WORSHIP, WHAT COMES TO MIND? DRAW OR LIST SOME OF THOSE HERE.

animate

THE WORD WORSHIP
MEANS WORTHINESS
OR "WORTH-SHIP." IN
OTHER WORDS, WE
WORSHIP SOMETHING
WHEN WE DEEM IT
WORTHY OF OUR TIME
AND ATTENTION.

MIKE SAYS THAT FOR HIM, COMMUNITY IS AN ESSENTIAL COMPONENT OF WORSHIP. WHAT ABOUT YOU? DO YOU CONSIDER YOURSELF MORE OF A SOLITARY WORSHIP PERSON OR THE COMMUNAL WORSHIP TYPE?

Make A list of a few of the things THAT are squeezing your HEART right now.

What solitary acts OF WORSHIP HELP LOOSEN the grip anxiety & fear have on your HEARt?

WhaT Role DOES YOUR FAITH COMMUNITY PLAY IN HELPING TO LOOSEN THAT GRIP?

How Does Your Worshipping Community work together to REBUILD, Restore and RENEW what's damaged and broken in the world?

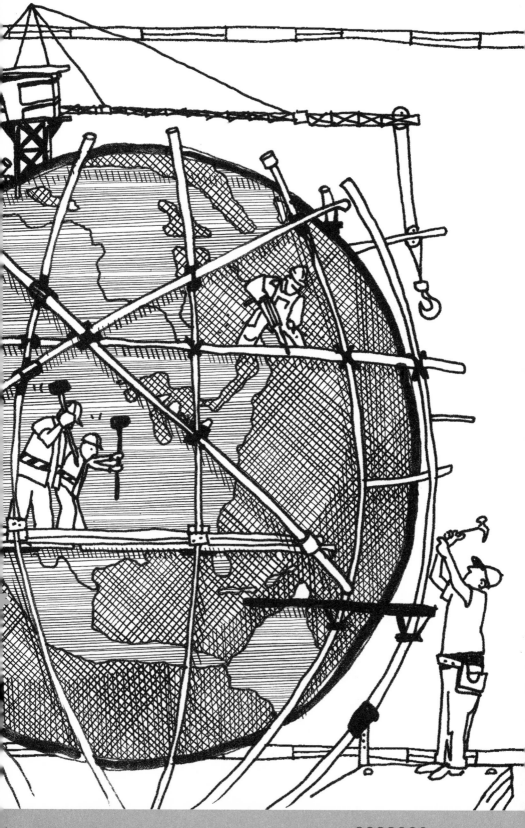

This week, you'll use simple acts of worship as a way of letting go of something that's gripping your heart. Today, go back to the journal page with the heart on it. Look at the list you made of things squeezing your heart and choose one that you want to focus on this week. Write it down and add any other thoughts you have on what's giving this issue the power to squeeze your heart. Anxiety? Fear? Lack of control? Whatever it is, name it.

" BUT OF COURSE There are all DIFFERENT KINDS OF *freedom*, and THE KIND that is MOST PRECIOUS YOU WILL NOT HEAR MUCH TALKED ABOUT IN THE GREAT OUTSIDE WORLD OF WINNING and ACHIEVING and DISPLAYING. THE *really* IMPORTANT KIND OF FREEDOM INVOLVES attention, AND awareness, and DISCIPLINE, and *effort*, AND BEING TRULY ABLE TO CARE ABOUT OTHER PEOPLE AND TO SACRIFICE FOR THEM, OVER AND OVER, IN MYRIAD PETTY LITtle UNSEXY WAYS, EVERY DAY. THAT IS REAL FREEDOM." —DAVID FOSTER WALLACE

DAY 2

Working to loosen the grip this issue has on you can be a little easier when you invite a friend to talk with you, pray for you, or just check in with you during the process. Today, talk to a friend about this effort. Give as much detail as you like, but be sure to tell your friend that you are being intentional about this effort and you'd like her to ask you about it in a few days, next week, a month from now. After you talk, write down your thoughts about that conversation. What did you notice as you named this issue out loud and shared it with someone?

"IF YOU WANT TO GO QUICKLY, GO ALONE. IF YOU WANT TO GO FAR, GO TOGETHER."
—AFRICAN PROVERB

"Come to Me, Take My Yoke upon you & learn from Me; for I am gentle and humble in heart, & you will find rest for your souls. for my yoke is easy & my burden is light."

Matthew 11: 28–30

Today, spend no more than 15 minutes writing about the issue you're working on. Jot down words that come to mind, fears or concerns, roadblocks, progress, whatever pops into your head. Don't over-think this exercise. Just write. Pay attention to the way the simple act of getting these words and thoughts out of your head and onto the page can help loosen their grip a bit.

animate

DAY 4

Choose three times today to pray about the issue you're working on. Use these times to pray for clarity, strength, and guidance. If prayer is hard for you, use the practice of centering prayer to get started. Just choose a word like "courage" or "patience" that names what you need most right now and pray that word. At the end of the day, write about how these prayers felt and what, if any, impact they had on your efforts to let go of this issue.

"during the time of prayer, we CONSENT to GOD'S PRESENCE AND ACTION WITHIN. at other times, OUR attention moves OUTWARD to discover GOD's presence EVERYWHERE."
—FR. THOMAS KEATING

Today, you're going to use meditation as a way of honing in on whatever has a hold on your heart. When you find yourself struggling with the fear or anxiety this issue brings, take a few moments to breath deeply and picture those fingers of fear slowly releasing their grip on you.
Focus on your breath as you breathe in strength and breathe out the pain. What do you notice as you practice this kind of intentional breathing and meditation?

"God's revelation... unmasks our illusions about ourselves. It exposes our pride, our individualism, our self-centeredness — in short, our sin. But worship also offers forgiveness, healing, transformation, motivation, and courage to work in the world for God's justice and peace — in short, salvation in its largest sense." —— MARVA DAWN

animate

DAY 6

Use this practice on the day you attend a worship service this week:
Do a little sociological study while your in church today. Notice the
ways prayer, singing, listening, and reflecting nudge your attention and
focus toward God. Which acts of corporate worship feel most meaningful
to you? How can this community and its worship practices help you heal
your heart?

"THAT IS WHAT WORSHIP IS ALL ABOUT.
IT IS THE GLAD SHOUT OF PRAISE THAT ARISES TO GOD
THE CREATOR AND GOD THE RESCUER
FROM THE CREATION THAT RECOGNIZES
ITS MAKER, THE CREATION THAT ACKNOWLEDGES THE
TRIUMPH OF JESUS THE LAMB,
THIS IS THE WORSHIP THAT IS GOING ON IN HEAVEN,
IN GOD'S DIMENSION, ALL THE TIME. THE
QUESTION WE OUGHT TO BE ASKING
IS HOW BEST MIGHT WE JOIN IN." —N.T. WRIGHT

SACRAMENTS | A TAPESTRY OF TRADITIONS
PHYLLIS TICKLE

PHYLLIS TICKLE

PHYLLIS TICKLE GREW UP PRESBYTERIAN AND JOINED THE EPISCOPAL CHURCH AS AN ADULT. SHE HAS WRITTEN EXTENSIVELY ABOUT RECLAIMING ANCIENT PRACTICES IN EVERYDAY LIFE, INCLUDING IN HER BEST-KNOWN BOOK, *THE DIVINE HOURS.*

SACRAMENTUM: THE MOST SERIOUS VOW THAT CAN EVER BE MADE

Phyllis unravels a bit of the knotted history of the Sacraments, tracing the threads all the way back to the Roman Empire. While the number and names of the Sacraments have changed over the course of church history, Phyllis reminds us that the meaning they hold has remained the same.

How does the historical meaning of the word *Sacrament* change your ideas about the role Sacraments play in the Christian faith?

PHYLLIS SUGGESTS THAT THE HISTORY OF THE SACRAMENTS IS LIKE A TAPESTRY THAT'S BEEN WOVEN TOGETHER THREAD-BY-THREAD OVER CENTURIES OF CHRISTIAN HISTORY...

...WE'RE STILL WEAVING THAT TAPESTRY TODAY, EVERY TIME WE PARTICIPATE IN A SACRAMENT.

Write DOWN SOME THOUGHTS about a time when taking COMMUNION OR WITNESSING a BAPTISM FELT LIKE a TRULY Spiritual experience FOR YOU. If THAT'S NEVER happened, WHAT WOULD IT TAKE FOR THOSE SACRAMENTS to HOLD DEEPER MEANING IN your Life?

THROUGHOUT THE HISTORY OF THE CHURCH, CHRISTIANS HAVE DEBATED WHETHER THE SACRAMENTS HAVE POWER UNTO THEMSELVES OR IF THEY ONLY HAVE POWER WHEN WE PERFORM THEM IN PARTICULAR WAYS. IN OTHER WORDS, IS IT *HOW* YOU DO IT OR *THAT* YOU DO IT THAT MATTERS?

For Phyllis, answering these questions is less important than our willingness to embrace the mystery embedded in the sacraments.

Why do we still get hung up on the logistics of the sacraments?

Where do you see the mystery of God's presence in communion? In baptism? In the other sacraments like confession and marriage?

:SAC

What DOES IT MEaN
To VISIBLY SEAL
OUR LIVES +o GOD —

ENTVM:

THROUGH the PRACTICE OF THE Sacraments?

This week, you'll be working through one of the less-common sacraments, confession. This might be a new practice for you or one that feels a little uncomfortable. That's okay. Each day, you'll move a bit deeper into the practice and have the chance to write about the feelings or thoughts it brings up. Today, think about a relationship in your life that might benefit from an act of confession on your part. Write down the name of the person you'd like to reconcile with over the course of this week as well as the part of your relationship that needs to heal.

"CONFESSION HEALS, CONFESSION JUSTIFIES, CONFESSION GRANTS PARDON of SIN, ALL HoPE CONSISTS IN CONFESSION; IN CONFESSION THERE IS A CHANCE FOR MERCY. BELIEVE IT FIRMLY, DO NOT DOUBT, DO NOT HESITATE, NEVER DESPAIR OF THE MERCY OF GOD." —ST. ISIDORE OF SEVILLE

Day 2

It's never easy to admit fault, but speaking our failures out loud can take some of their power and shame away. Start the process of confession by talking honestly with God about the issue. Confess out loud to God and allow yourself to feel God's grace work its way into you. What is this experience like for you?

66 a lot of people refuse to do things because they don't want to go *naked*, don't want to go WITHOUT *guarantee*. But that's what's got to happen. You go NAKED until You Die. 99
— NIKKI GIOVANNI

It can help to bring another person into this process to offer support and encouragement. Today, ask a trusted friend or your pastor to listen to your confession. Journal a bit about what might be holding you back from moving more deeply into this practice.

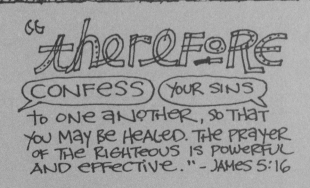

Day 4

Now it gets real. Reach out to the person you need to confess to and ask to meet tomorrow. If it's not possible to get together in person, set up a time to talk on the phone or over Skype. No texting or email allowed here—this needs to happen in a face-to-face conversation. Write out any fears or anxieties you have about this step. And don't forget to lean on the person you asked to support you. This is when you'll need them most.

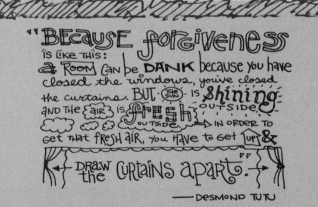

"BECAUSE forgiveness is like this: a room can be DANK because you have closed the windows, you've closed the curtains. BUT (sun) is shining and the {air} is FRESH outside. (outside) In order to get that fresh air, you have to get {up} & draw the curtains apart."

—DESMOND TUTU

 **Day 5**

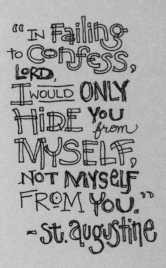

"In failing to confess, Lord, I would only hide you from myself, not myself from you."
— St. Augustine

This is the day you make it happen. As you confess, keep the focus on you and the actions you regret. Ask your friend to listen and allow you to say what you need to say. Ask for forgiveness. You might not get it, but no matter what happens as a result of this confession, you will have made a significant step toward repairing a broken relationship. Then take some time to write down your thoughts about this conversation. How did it feel? What did you hope for? What might come from this?

Day 6

Today, take some time to reflect and write about this experience. Allow yourself to feel that weight of guilt lift off of you, no matter how the conversation went. You might not have gotten the response you hoped for from the other person, but you can find rest and peace in the grace of God.

"Let us therefore approach the throne of grace with BOLDNESS, so that we may receive mercy and find grace to help in time of need."

—Hebrews 4:16

MONEY | THE JOY OF SHARING
SHANE CLAIBORNE

SHANE CLAIBORNE IS AN ACTIVIST,
AN AUTHOR, AND THE FOUNDER OF THE
SIMPLE WAY, A FAITH COMMUNITY IN
INNER-CITY PHILADELPHIA.
HIS BOOKS INCLUDE *THE IRRESISTIBLE
REVOLUTION* AND *JESUS FOR PRESIDENT*.
AS IF THAT WEREN'T ENOUGH, HE ALSO
MAKES HIS OWN CLOTHES, JUGGLES,
AND BREATHES FIRE.

Shane asks us to think about something most of us would rather not think about—our often insatiable need to be successful, to have money and other material possession, and to gain a sense of power in the world. What makes this subject hard to talk about?

SHANE SUGGESTS WE NEED A "THEOLOGY OF ENOUGH." WHAT DO YOU THINK HE MEANS BY THAT?

OVER KILL

TONS

LOTS

ENOUGH

ALMOST ENOUGH

NEED MORE

NADA

At what point in your life did you start to worry about having "enough"? Where does that anxiety come from?

In what ways could having a theology of enough be freeing for you?

This is what

WE ALL HAVE HURDLES THAT KEEP US FROM SHARING WHAT WE HAVE—
WE DON'T KNOW HOW TO ASK FOR HELP, WE HAVE A HARD TIME
GIVING SOMETHING AWAY, WE WORRY WE'LL COME UP SHORT IF WE
GIVE TOO MUCH. WHAT MIGHT BE STOPPING YOU FROM SHARING?

Shane says we are made for love,
compassion, and community. How do you
see these "built-in" traits playing out in
your life?

> « **all** who believed were together and had all things in common; they would sell their possessions and goods and distribute the proceeds to all, as any had need. Day by day, as they spent much time together in the temple, they broke bread and ate their food with glad and generous hearts. » —ACTS 2:44-46

animate

THE BEST THINGS IN LIFE IS TO _____ AWAY.

How can you practice generosity today?

DAY 1

This week, you'll begin a practice meant to build your sharing muscles, particularly as they apply to money. If you don't already have a system for tracking your spending, grab a notebook, open an Excel document, or just find an old envelope, and use it to write down every cent you spend this week. It seems sort of obsessive/compulsive, but it's the best way to see where your money goes. And that's the key to figuring out where you want your money to go. Before you start, write down your guesses about what you spend the most money on each week.

"A BONE TO THE DOG IS NOT CHARITY. CHARITY IS THE BONE SHARED WITH THE DOG, WHEN YOU ARE JUST AS HUNGRY AS THE DOG."
— Jack London

DAY 2

Now that you're tracking your spending, take some time today to consider how you could share some of what you have. Brainstorm some possible ways to share your financial resources with others. It might be as simple as a donation to an organization that's meaningful to you or as long-term as starting a fund to send a child to camp or college. Write down some ideas here.

"You are forgiven for your happiness and your successes only if you generously consent to share them."
~ Albert Camus

DAY 3

Generosity, particularly when it involves money, is often easier to practice when you're doing so with other people. So today, invite a friend or two to join in your efforts to share a bit of what you have. What new options for sharing become possible when you pool your resources with those of other people?

"for pleasure has no relish unless we share it."
— VIRGINIA WOOLF.

animate

DAY 4

Today, start dreaming a little bigger. As you think about personal acts of generosity, what ideas come to mind about more communal efforts? What could your family do? Your neighborhood? Your faith community? Write down some ideas here.

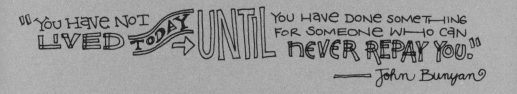

"YOU HAVE NOT LIVED TODAY → UNTIL YOU HAVE DONE SOMETHING FOR SOMEONE WHO CAN NEVER REPAY YOU."
— John Bunyan

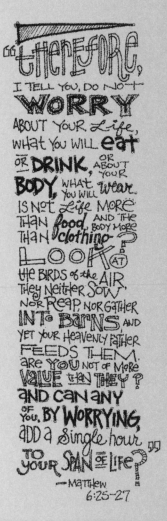

"Therefore, I TELL YOU, DO NOT WORRY ABOUT YOUR *Life*, WHAT YOU WILL **eat** OR **DRINK**, OR ABOUT YOUR **BODY**, WHAT YOU WILL *wear.* IS NOT *Life* MORE THAN *food*, AND THE BODY MORE THAN *clothing*? LOOK AT tHe BIRDS of tHe AIR, THey NeitHer SOW, NOR REAP, NOR GATHER **INTO BARNS**, AND YET YOUR HEAVENLY FATHER FEEDS THEM. aRe YOU NOT OF MORE **VALUE** THAN THEY? AND CAN ANY OF YOU, BY WORRYING, ADD a *single hour* TO YOUR SPAN OF LIFE?"

— MATTHEW 6:25-27

The focus of this practice has been on money, but there are other ways to live into the "theology of enough" that go beyond finances. Today, think about what it means for you to have enough. Take an inventory of your house, your closet, your relationships. What does it mean to have "enough" in these areas? Why does contentment so often feel out of reach?

DAY 6

Now that you've identified where your money really goes each week, as well as a way to share some of what you have, think about how much you could realistically share on a regular basis. Write down your "pledge" here along with some thoughts on what it might cost you to share your financial resources with others. What are you going to have to give up?

"WHEN we STRUGGLE FOR HUMAN RIGHTS FOR FREEDOM, FOR DIGNITY, when we feel that it is a MINISTRY OF the CHURCH TO CONCERN ITSELF WITH THOSE WHO ARE HUNGRY, FOR THOSE WHO HAVE NO SCHOOLS, for those who are DEPRIVED, WE ARE NOT DEPARTING FROM GOD'S PROMISE. HE COMES TO FREE US FROM SIN, AND THE CHURCH KNOWS THAT SIN'S CONSEQUENCES ARE ALL SUCH INJUSTICES AND ABUSES. THE CHURCH KNOWS IT IS SAVING THE WORLD WHEN IT UNDERTAKES TO SPEAK ALSO OF SUCH THINGS."

— OSCAR A. ROMERO

SERVICE | THE NEEDS RIGHT AROUND YOU
ENUMA OKORO

ENUMA OKORO IS A POET, SPEAKER, AND AUTHOR. SHE SPENT HER CHILDHOOD IN NIGERIA AND ENGLAND, WENT TO COLLEGE IN MINNESOTA, AND NOW SPLITS HER TIME BETWEEN NORTH CAROLINA AND NIGERIA. SHE IS THE AUTHOR OF *A RELUCTANT PILGRIM* AND *SILENCE AND OTHER SURPRISING INVITATIONS OF ADVENT*.

What assumptions have you made about what service looks like? Do you have to get on a plane to do "real" service? Do you have to suffer for it to count?

THERE IS OVERWHELMING
NEED IN THE WORLD AND
THAT CAN SOMETIMES
PARALYZE US AND KEEP US
FROM ACTION. BUT IF WE
FOCUS OUR ATTENTION ON
THE SMALLER PICTURE, WE
OFTEN SEE PLACES OF NEEI
THAT HAVE BEEN RIGHT IN
FRONT OF US ALL ALONG.

Service

isn't just something we do for other people. It changes us by shifting our TIME, ATTENTION, and resources to something other than ourselves. **HOW** might practicing intentional acts of service start to change your perspective? your neighborhood? YOUR WORK PLACE? YOUR COMMUNITY?

ENUMA SAYS, "WHEN PEOPLE SERVE OTHERS, THE WORLD GETS A GLIMPSE OF GOD." JESUS BROUGHT THE DEAD TO LIFE AND TURNED WATER INTO WINE. BUT HIS ACTS OF SERVICE WEREN'T ALWAYS GRAND MIRACLES.

JESUS SHOWED US THAT SERVICE CAN BE AS SIMPLE AND PROFOUND AS WASHING SOMEONE'S DIRTY FEET, TOUCHING THE "UNTOUCHABLES," OR TALKING TO AN UNPOPULAR TAX COLLECTOR.

animate

BUS

Helping old Lady on Bus

DOWN TOWN

So if I, your Lord & Teacher, have washed your feet, you also OUGHT to wash one another's feet. For I have set you as an example, that you also should do as I have done TO YOU.
~John 13:14-15

Raking Leaves

what are some simple acts of service you have done or could do for the people in your life?

Giving a homeless man a coffee

animate

Day 1

Since serving is rooted in seeing, use this week to start seeing some areas of need in your community that you could address through your service. Look around your neighborhood for someone who could use help around the house or benefit from some coffee and conversation. Pay attention to the "regulars" on your route to work—the homeless woman, the worn-out bagel guy, the awkward teenager on the bus. List some simple ways you could serve some of these people.

"Everybody can be great because everybody can serve. You don't have to have a college degree to serve. You don't have to make your subject & verb agree to serve... You only need a heart full of **Grace**, a soul generated by **Love**. **You** can be that servant." Martin Luther King, Jr.

Day 2

Individual acts of service aren't your only option. Today, do some research into organizations in your area that use volunteers. Which groups might be a good fit for you? Choose two or three that seem appealing and contact them. Set up a time to visit the organization or meet with someone who works there in the next day or two. Get a feel for what the organization needs and how you might be able to help out. Write down the names and contact numbers here:

This is what you shall do; Love the earth & sun and the animals, despise riches, give alms to everyone that asks, stand up for the stupid and crazy, devote your income & labor to others, hate tyrants, argue not concerning **God**, have patience & indulgence toward people..."

~Walt Whitman

Day 3

Whether you're doing a more personal act of service or volunteering with an organization, get the ball rolling and put those good intentions into action today. Buy a sandwich for that homeless woman, shovel your neighbor's sidewalk, schedule your first shift as a volunteer. Write about how that experience went.

"HOW DOES GOD'S LOVE ABIDE IN ANYONE WHO HAS THE WORLD'S GOODS AND SEES A BROTHER OR SISTER IN NEED & YET REFUSES HELP?"

—I JOHN 3:17

animate

If serving someone else feels like more than you can manage, take some time today to do an honest inventory of what's using up your time and energy. What are you doing that's keeping you from practicing an act of service in your neighborhood or community?

"REMEMBER that when you leave this earth, you can take with you NOTHING that you have received⁓ fading symbols of honor, trappings of power⁓ but only what you have been given: a full heart enriched by honest service, love, sacrifice and courage."

—Saint Francis of Assisi

Day 5

MAY THE HOLY SPIRIT GUIDE & STRENGTHEN ME, THAT IN THIS, AND IN ALL THINGS, I MAY DO GOD'S WILL IN THE SERVICE OF THE KINGDOM OF HIS CHRIST. AMEN.
—ADAPTED FROM THE BOOK OF COMMON PRAYER

By today, you should have either acted on your plan or be preparing to do so in the next few days. That makes this a great day to consider how you're feeling about this process. What things feel uncomfortable as you prepare to step into an environment or a relationship that's unfamiliar? What are you excited about?

Day 6

Today, consider how you can make this week's act of service a regular part of your life. What would it look like to help that neighbor for an hour every week? To develop a friendly connection with the bagel guy? To commit to an organization for the next month or even year?
Think about how you can incorporate this practice into your life over the long haul. What parts of your normal routine might have to change for that to happen?

"**CHRIST** HAS NO BODY HERE ON EARTH BUT **YOURS.** NO HANDS BUT YOURS. NO FEET BUT YOURS. YOURS ARE THE **EYES** WHICH EXPRESS CHRIST'S COMPASSION TO THE **WORLD.** Yours are the feet WITH WHICH CHRIST is to GO ABOUT DOING GOOD. AND yours ARE THE HANDS WITH WHICH CHRIST is to BLESS US NOW."

~ TERESA OF avila

animate

COMMUNITY | AN UNEXPECTED FAMILY
DOUG PAGITT

Doug Pagitt

DOUG PAGITT IS THE FOUNDING PASTOR OF SOLOMON'S PORCH, A FAITH COMMUNITY IN MINNEAPOLIS. HE IS THE AUTHOR OF SEVERAL BOOKS, INCLUDING *A CHRISTIANITY WORTH BELIEVING* AND *COMMUNITY IN THE INVENTIVE AGE.* HE STARTED RUNNING TWO YEARS AGO AND NOW RUNS ULTRA MARATHONS.

"IN ONE afternoon, THESE BoyS Went FRoM BEiNG OUR neighBoRs to being our Family. "

Think about the first time you walked into the church you attend now. What was that like? What did it—or would it—take for you to feel at home there?

"Community is all about PARTICIPATION. It's about creating BIG, OPEN, welcoming spaces that INVITE and EVEN DEMAND PARTICIPATION from EVERYONE who shows up."

— DOUG

PARTICIPANT 3721

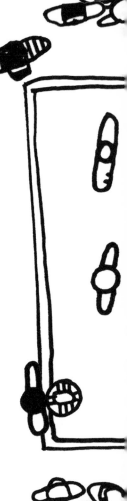

HOW DO YOU LEAVE THE SIDELINES AND GET IN THE GAME?

List three ways your church has helped you become a participant in the community and not just a spectator.

If you still feel like a spectator, what kind of invitation do you need to get involved?

IN THE STORY OF PETER AND CORNELIUS IN ACTS 10, BOTH MEN HAD TO OVERCOME SERIOUS OBSTACLES IN ORDER TO SHARE FRIENDSHIP AND EVEN FAITH. WHO DO YOU KNOW WHO MIGHT NEED TO OVERCOME SOMETHING IN ORDER TO ENTER MORE FULLY INTO YOUR FAITH COMMUNITY? HOW CAN YOU OPEN UP THE GATE AND WELCOME THEM IN?

OKay!

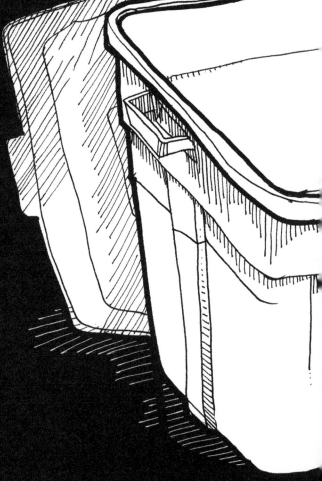

WHAT DO YOU
BRING WITH Y
TO YOUR COMMUN

This week, you'll dig into the practice of community by finding ways to use your passions, talents, and connections in your church. Some people have a hard time with this—they feel like they aren't invited or welcomed to involve themselves in their faith community. So start in this practice by writing down some thoughts about what might hold you back from investing yourself in your church. What could you do to get over some of these hurdles?

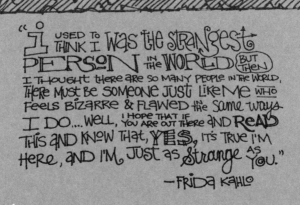

"I used to think I was the strangest person in the world (but then) I thought there are so many people in the world, there must be someone just like me who feels bizarre & flawed the same ways I do.... Well, I hope that if you are out there and read this and know that, YES, it's true I'm here, and I'm just as strange as you."

—FRIDA KAHLO

Remember that tub you filled up on the previous page? Look over what you wrote. Now get specific about the talents or interests or resources you have that could help you get more involved in your faith community. Think creatively: Maybe you're good with money and could offer to teach a class on budgeting or investments. Maybe you've raised your kids already and could mentor a younger parent. Maybe you live close to the airport and can offer rides when people need to fly somewhere. Write down some options below.

"One of the MARVELOUS things about community is that it enables us to WELCOME AND HELP people in a way we couldn't as individuals. When we POOL our STRENGTH and SHARE the work and responsibility, we can welcome MANY people, even those in deep distress, and perhaps help them find SELF-CONFIDENCE and INNER HEALING."
— JEAN VANIER

DAY 3

Today, head to your church's website or send an email to the person facilitating your Animate classes to find out what opportunities for involvement already exist in your faith community. You don't need to commit to anything yet, but don't rule anything out either. Just get a sense of what's already going on in your community. Make some notes here about places you can see yourself using the skills and interests you listed yesterday.

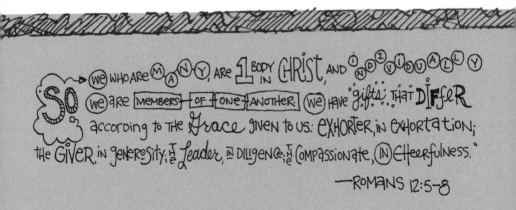

"**SO** ➤ (WE) WHO ARE M A N Y, ARE **1** BODY IN CHRIST, AND I N D I V I D U A L L Y (WE) ARE MEMBERS OF ONE ANOTHER (WE) HAVE *gifts* THAT DIFFER according to THE *Grace* given to us: EXHORTER, IN EXHORTATION; the GIVER, IN generosity; the *Leader*, IN DILIGENCE; the COMPASSIONATE, (IN) CHeerfulness."

—ROMANS 12:5–8

DAY 4

Now that you've got a sense of what you can offer and what's already happening in your community, take today to pray or talk to a friend or two about taking the big step toward true involvement. What feels scary about this? What feels hopeful?

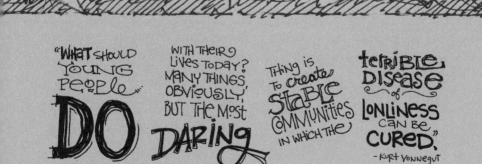

"WHAT SHOULD YOUNG PEOPLE DO WITH THEIR LIVES TODAY? MANY THINGS, OBVIOUSLY, BUT THE MOST DARING THING IS TO create STABLE COMMUNITIES IN WHICH THE terrible DISEASE of LONLINESS CAN BE CURED."
– KURT VONNEGUT

If you get this far and just haven't found something that feels like a good fit for you, consider how you might create that fit. If you brew your own beer or have a knack for gardening or tell great stories, think about how those skills could create new ways for you—and others—to connect in your community. Write down your thoughts here.

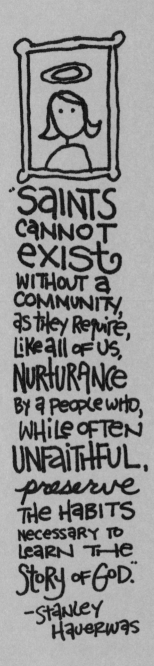

"SAINTS CANNOT EXIST WITHOUT A COMMUNITY, as they require, Like all of us, NURTURANCE By a people who, WHILE OFTEN UNFAITHFUL, preserve THE HABITS necessary to LEARN THE STORY OF GOD."
—STANLEY HAUERWAS

DAY 6

This is the day to take action. If there's a group at church you'd like to join, call or text the person coordinating that group and let them know you're interested. If you've got an idea for a new event or project in your faith community, arrange to meet with the pastor to talk about how you can make that happen. As you get started, come back to this page and write about how it's going. What are you learning about community? About yourself?

"Life will break you. Nobody can protect you from that, and living alone won't either, for solitude will also break you with—its yearning. You have to love. You have to feel. It is the reason you are here on earth. You are here to risk your heart. You are here to be swallowed up."

—Louise Erdrich

animate

Notes

animate <

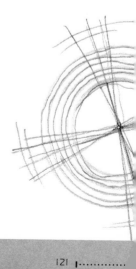

animate

notes

ISBN 978-1-4514-9006-0